© IPC Magazines Ltd., 1985

3

4

5

6

7

13

14

15

18

19

SPOT THE DIFFERENCE!

Our artist has made TEN alterations to Picture 'B'. Can you spot them? Answers at foot of the page.

ANSWERS: 1. Balloon top left is now black. 2. Santa's coat. 3. Berry missing from Christmas pud. 4. Extra band around cake. 5. Label gone from cracker. 6. Extra mince pie. 7. Middle prong gone from dad's fork. 8. Bauble missing from tree. 9. Black spots on mum's dress. 10. Decoration missing top right.

21

24

25

27

28

29

IT'S PUZZLE TIME

THERE ARE 25 ANIMALS HIDDEN IN THE *WORD BALLOONS* IN THIS STORY. WE'VE *UNDERLINED* THE FIRST ONE TO START YOU OFF! CAN YOU FIND THE OTHER 24? (PIC 2—'CRAB' DOESN'T COUNT.)

ANSWERS: PICTURE 1: BEAVER, DOG, GOAT, FOX, OX; PICTURE 2: SEAL, RABBIT, TORTOISE; PICTURE 3: CAT, HARE, HORSE, CAMEL; PICTURE 4: RAT, HAMSTER, OTTER, DEER, ANTEATER; PICTURE 5: PIG, BAT, HEDGEHOG; PICTURE 6: PANTHER, MOOSE, FROG, LLAMA.

Bumpkin Billionaires

35

37

39

41

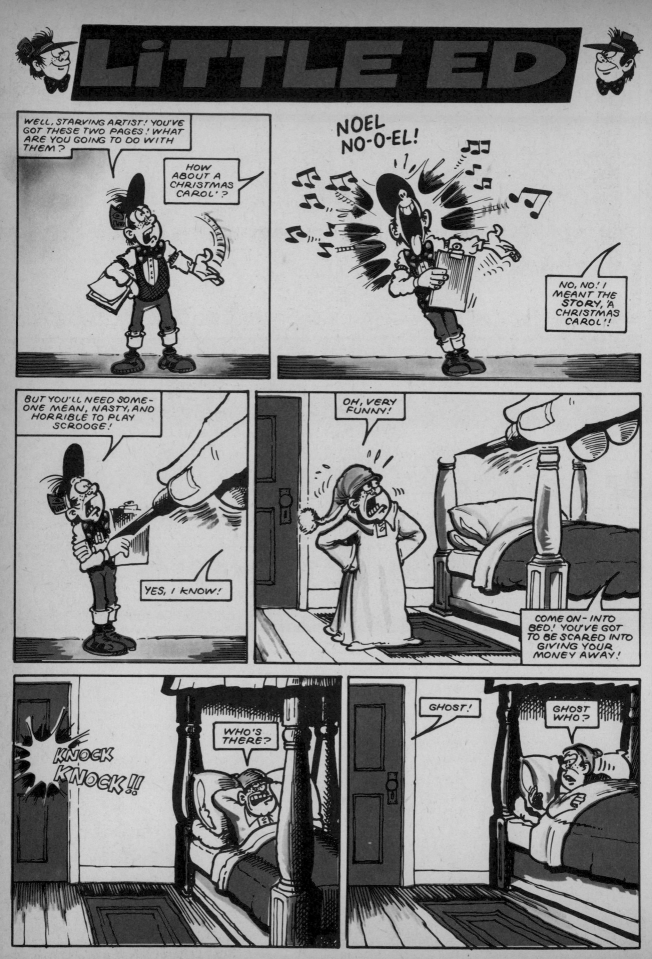

43

44

45

His mum said, "Sid! Now eat your greens!
They'll bring colour to your cheeks!"
But Sid sat sulking, still and sad,
And wouldn't touch his leeks.

At school, the dinner-lady tried
To make him eat his custard—
He promptly slopped it on the floor—
She really was disgusted!

But Sid was getting hungry now
And his tum began to rumble—
But still he wouldn't eat pork chops
With chips, or rhubarb crumble!

Then one fine day, to mum's surprise
Our Sid said, "They look great!
I think I'll have a bowl of those!"
So mum piled up his plate!

What was it, then, that Sid had seen,
Which finally won him over?
A box of crunchy biscuits bought
By mum for Sid's dog, Rover!

Now Sid won't touch the doggy nosh
Not even for a lark!
A dog's life wasn't for our lad
But you should have heard him bark!

48

49

50

52

53

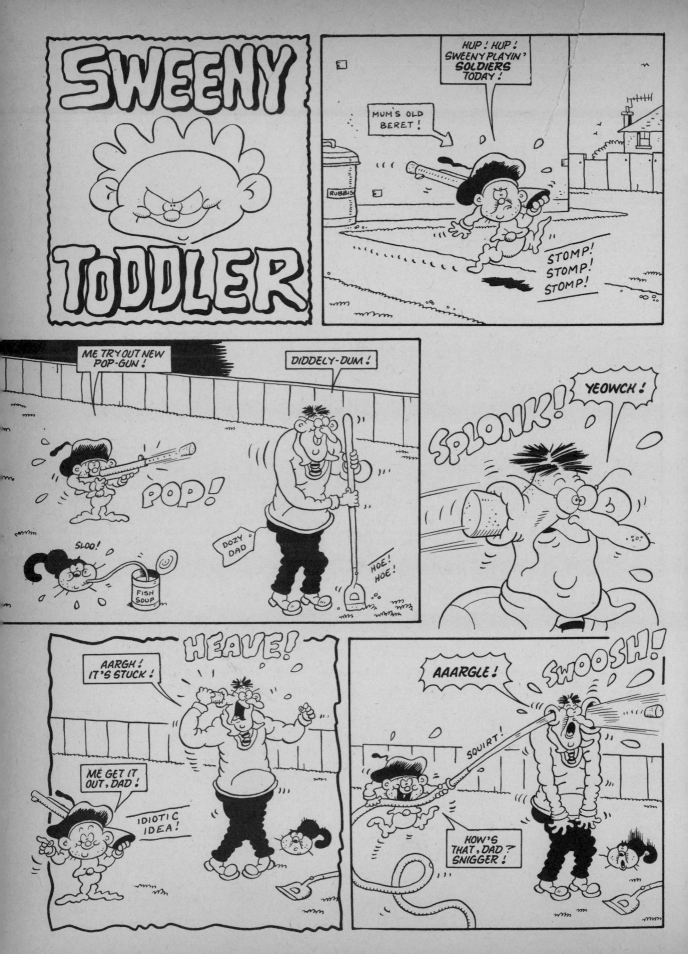

54

55

SANTA HASN'T NOTICED THAT HIS SACK HAS A *HOLE* IN IT, AND NOW ALL THE PRESENTS ARE *LOST* IN THE SNOW! IT'S UP TO *YOU* TO HELP *TOY BOY* TO RECOVER THE GIFTS IN TIME FOR CHRISTMAS MORNING!

YOU WILL NEED:
ONE DICE; ONE TOKEN FOR EACH PLAYER (USE COUNTERS OR BUTTONS); TEN COINS.

HOW TO PLAY:
1. PUT PLAYERS' TOKENS ON *START*. PLACE ONE *COIN* ON EACH OF THE *TOYS* ON THE BOARD.
2. PLAYERS TAKE TURNS IN THROWING THE DICE AND MOVING THEIR TOKENS ALONG THE TRACK.
3. THE PLAYER WHO FIRST REACHES ANY *COIN* MUST *STOP* THERE (EVEN IF THE THROW WOULD HAVE TAKEN THE TOKEN PAST THIS SPACE). THE PLAYER *TAKES THE COIN* (TO SHOW THAT THE TOY HAS BEEN *FOUND*) AND THIS ENDS HIS/HER TURN. OF COURSE, THE TOY MUST BE DUG FROM THE SNOW, SO THE PLAYER MUST *MISS THE NEXT TURN!*
4. WHEN A COIN HAS BEEN *REMOVED*, THE SPACE IS TREATED AS AN ORDINARY SPACE, AND THE REMAINING PLAYERS MAY PASS IT AS USUAL.
5. THE GAME *ENDS* AS SOON AS ONE PLAYER REACHES THE *FINISH* AND DELIVERS THE TOYS BACK TO SANTA. YOU DO *NOT* HAVE TO LAND ON *FINISH* EXACTLY!
6. ALL PLAYERS NOW COUNT THEIR COINS TO SEE HOW MANY TOYS THEY HAVE COLLECTED. THE PLAYER WHO REACHED THE FINISH *DOUBLES* THE TOTAL OF HIS/HER COINS!
7. THE PLAYER WITH THE *HIGHEST TOTAL* IS THE *WINNER!* IF TWO OR MORE PLAYERS *TIE* FOR THE HIGHEST SCORE, THOSE PLAYERS MUST PLAY THE GAME AGAIN TO DECIDE THE WINNER!

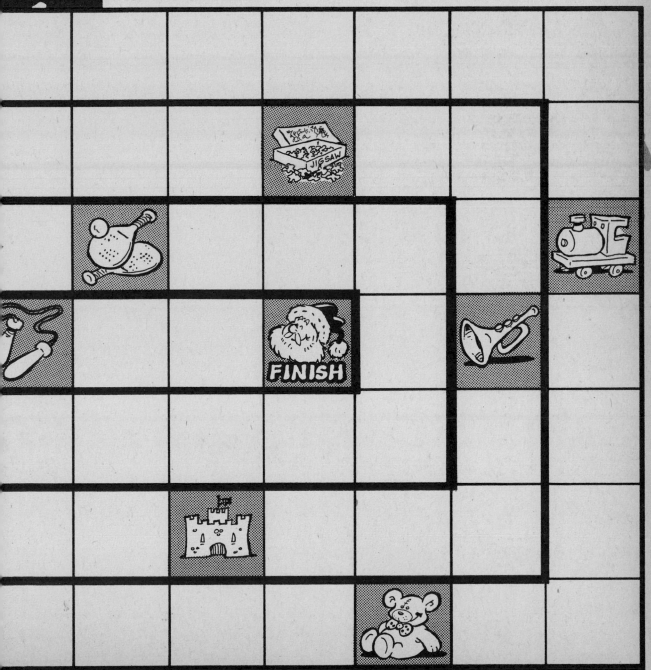

59

60

61

SPOT THE DIFFERENCE!

Our artist has made TEN alterations to Picture 'B'. Can you spot them? Answers at foot of the page.

ANSWERS: 1, Bauble missing near top of tree. 2, The word 'choc' missing from box on tree. 3, Lower bauble now a star. 4, 'S' missing from Bookworm's book. 5, Black stripe on parcel. 6, Spots have appeared on 'plain' parcel. 7, One of Dad's shoes has turned black. 8, A mousehole has appeared in the skirting board. 9, Light-switch has gone. 10, Star now hanging from decorations.

70

ANIMALAD

75

77

81

83

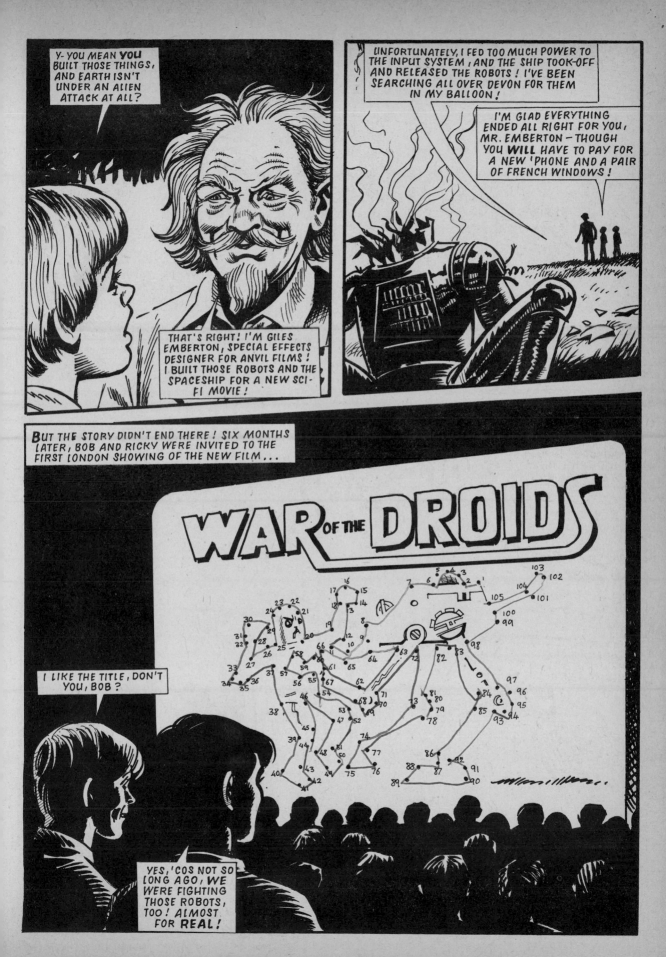

89

91

93

94

IT'S PUZZLE TIME

THESE COMIC CHARACTERS ARE ACTING OUT NINE FAMOUS PROVERBS! CAN YOU GUESS WHAT THEY ARE? TO HELP YOU, EACH PROVERB IS GIVEN IN THE CAPTION, BUT WE'VE ONLY GIVEN THE FIRST LETTERS OF THE IMPORTANT WORDS.

1. *L* BEFORE YOU *L*.

2. DON'T *C* YOUR *C* BEFORE THEY'RE *H*.

EGGS

3. TOO MANY *C* *S* THE *B*.

YUCK!

4. A *S* IN *T S N*.

OWW! MY SIDE HURTS! NOW I WON'T HAVE TO RUN THE REST OF THE RACE!

FINISH 9 MILES

5. MANY *H* MAKE *L W*.

CLICK!

6. A *B* IN THE *H* IS *W T* IN THE *B*.

PRICE £10
PRICE £5
PRICE £5

7. ALL *W* AND NO *P* MAKES *J* A *DB*.

I'M TOO BUSY TO GO TO THE THEATRE!

8. A *R S* GATHERS *N M*.

YOU'LL NEVER GET ANYTHING LIKE THAT!

9. HE WHO *H* IS *L*.

IT'S TOO DARK TO FIND MY WAY HOME!

I CALCULATE YOU SHOULD HAVE LEFT SOONER!

edward oliver

ANSWERS: 1. LOOK BEFORE YOU LEAP; 2. DON'T COUNT YOUR CHICKENS BEFORE THEY'RE HATCHED; 3. TOO MANY COOKS SPOIL THE BROTH; 4. A STITCH IN TIME SAVES NINE; 5. MANY HANDS MAKE LIGHT WORK; 6. A BIRD IN THE HAND IS WORTH TWO IN THE BUSH; 7. ALL WORK AND NO PLAY MAKES JACK A DULL BOY; 8. A ROLLING STONE GATHERS NO MOSS; 9. HE WHO HESITATES IS LOST.

95

97

FRANK McDIARMID

101

102

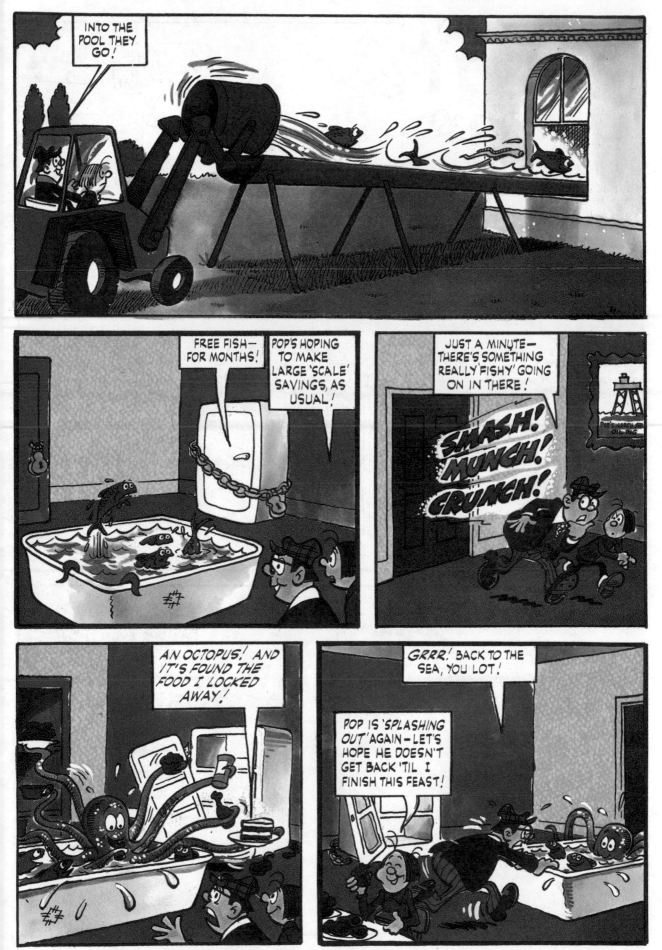

105